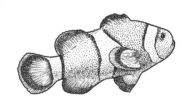

# A VISIT TO THE
# ZOO
# Field Trip
# Journal

## Observe and Study

## 50 Amazing Animals

FUNSCHOOLING.COM

By Sarah Janisse Brown and International Illustrators

# HOW TO USE THIS BOOK:

1. Take this research journal to the zoo each time you go!

2. Write down what you learn about each animal that you see!

3. Pictures of 35 common zoo animals are already included in this journal. If you find an animal that is not in this book add your own drawing of the animal or tape a photo onto the page.

4. Bring colored pencils with you to the zoo if you would like to draw or color an animal while observing it.

5. To learn more about each animal read the signs posted at each exhibit and talk to a zookeeper. They are happy to answer questions.

6. This Journal can last several years, keep it in a safe place and use it every time to go to the zoo.

7. If you would like to learn more about any of the animals you see you can read books or watch documentaries at home.

NAME & AGE _____

CONTACT INFORMATION: _____

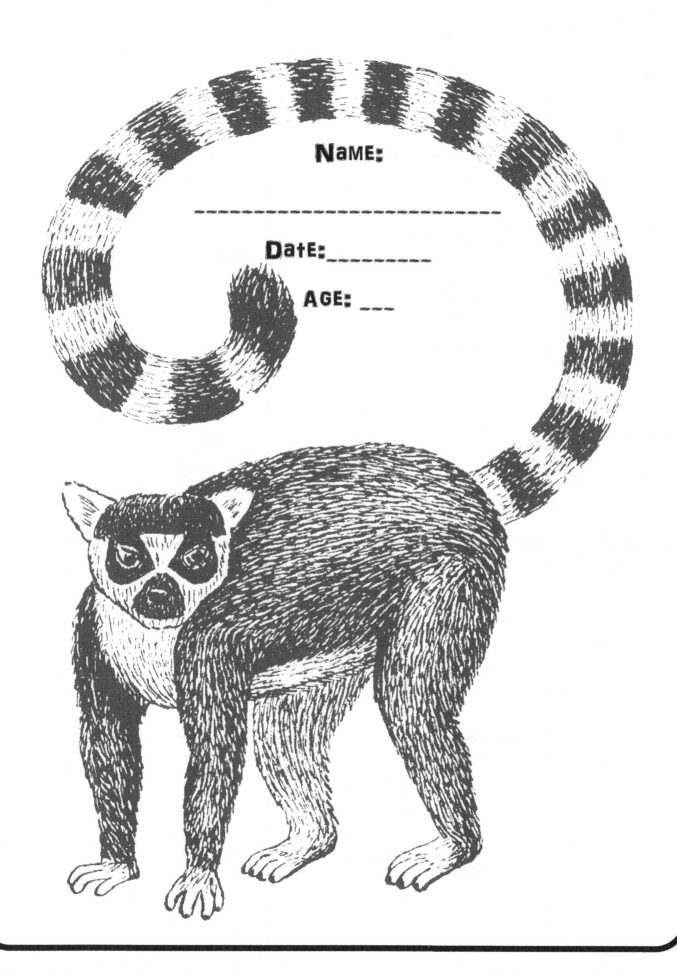

NaME:

_ _ _ _ _ _ _ _ _ _ _ _ _ _ _ _ _ _ _ _ _ _ _

DatE:_ _ _ _ _ _ _ _

AGE: _ _ _

| 56 | 58 | 60 | 62 | 64 |
|---|---|---|---|---|
| | | | | |
| 66 | 68 | 70 | 72 | 74 |
| | | | | |
| 76 | 78 | 80 | 82 | 84 |
| | | | | |
| 86 | 88 | 90 | 92 | 94 |
| | | | | |
| 96 | 98 | 100 | 102 | 104 |
| | | | | |

Name of Zoo:_____

City and State:_____

Time and Date:_____

Name of Exhibit:_____

Type of Animal:_____

Interesting Observations:

_____
_____
_____
_____
_____
_____

# Today I saw a:

## Draw its natural habitat:

## Draw its enclosure:

## My Notes:

_____
_____
_____
_____
_____
_____
_____
_____
_____
_____
_____
_____

## Meal at the zoo:

## Meal in the wild:

Name of Zoo:_____

City and State:_____

Time and Date:_____

Name of Exhibit:_____

Type of Animal:_____

Interesting Observations:

_____
_____
_____
_____
_____
_____

# Today I saw a:

## Draw its natural habitat:

## Draw its enclosure:

## My Notes:

_____
_____
_____
_____
_____
_____
_____
_____
_____
_____
_____
_____
_____

## Meal at the zoo:

## Meal in the wild:

Name of Zoo:_____

City and State: _____

Time and Date:_____

Name of Exhibit:_____

Type of Animal:_____

### Interesting Observations:

_____
_____
_____
_____
_____
_____

Today I saw a:

Draw its natural habitat:

Draw its enclosure:

My Notes:

_____
_____
_____
_____
_____
_____
_____
_____
_____
_____
_____
_____
_____

Meal at the zoo:

Meal in the wild:

Name of Zoo:_____

City and State:_____

Time and Date:_____

Name of Exhibit:_____

Type of Animal:_____

### Interesting Observations:

_____
_____
_____
_____
_____
_____

Today I saw a:

Draw its natural habitat:

Draw its enclosure:

My Notes:

_____
_____
_____
_____
_____
_____
_____
_____
_____
_____
_____
_____

Meal at the zoo:

Meal in the wild:

Name of Zoo:_____

City and State: _____

Time and Date:_____

Name of Exhibit:_____

Type of Animal:_____

Interesting Observations:

_____
_____
_____
_____
_____
_____

Today I saw a:

Draw its natural habitat:

Draw its enclosure:

My Notes:

_____
_____
_____
_____
_____
_____
_____
_____
_____
_____
_____
_____
_____

Meal at the zoo:

Meal in the wild:

Name of Zoo:_____

City and State:_____

Time and Date:_____

Name of Exhibit:_____

Type of Animal:_____

### Interesting Observations:

_____
_____
_____
_____
_____
_____
_____

# Today I saw a:

17

## Draw its natural habitat:

## Draw its enclosure:

## My Notes:

_____
_____
_____
_____
_____
_____
_____
_____
_____
_____
_____
_____
_____

## Meal at the zoo:

## Meal in the wild:

Name of Zoo:_____

City and State:_____

Time and Date:_____

Name of Exhibit:_____

Type of Animal:_____

### Interesting Observations:

_____
_____
_____
_____
_____
_____

# Today I saw a:

19

## Draw its natural habitat:

## Draw its enclosure:

## My Notes:

_____
_____
_____
_____
_____
_____
_____
_____
_____
_____
_____
_____

## Meal at the zoo:

## Meal in the wild:

Name of Zoo:_____

City and State:_____

Time and Date:_____

Name of Exhibit:_____

Type of Animal:_____

Interesting Observations:

_____
_____
_____
_____
_____
_____

# Today I saw a:

## Draw its natural habitat:

## Draw its enclosure:

## My Notes:

_____
_____
_____
_____
_____
_____
_____
_____
_____
_____
_____
_____
_____

## Meal at the zoo:

## Meal in the wild:

Name of Zoo:_____

City and State:_____

Time and Date:_____

Name of Exhibit:_____

Type of Animal:_____

Interesting Observations:

_____
_____
_____
_____
_____
_____
_____

Today I saw a:

Draw its natural habitat:

Draw its enclosure:

My Notes:

_____
_____
_____
_____
_____
_____
_____
_____
_____
_____
_____
_____
_____

Meal at the zoo:

Meal in the wild:

Name of Zoo:_____

City and State:_____

Time and Date:_____

Name of Exhibit:_____

Type of Animal:_____

### Interesting Observations:

_____
_____
_____
_____
_____
_____
_____

Today I saw a:

Draw its natural habitat:

Draw its enclosure:

My Notes:

Meal at the zoo:

Meal in the wild:

Name of Zoo:_____

City and State:_____

Time and Date:_____

Name of Exhibit:_____

Type of Animal:_____

Interesting Observations:

_____
_____
_____
_____
_____
_____

## Today I saw a:

27

## Draw its natural habitat:

## Draw its enclosure:

## My Notes:

_____
_____
_____
_____
_____
_____
_____
_____
_____
_____
_____
_____
_____

## Meal at the zoo:

## Meal in the wild:

Name of Zoo:_____

City and State:_____

Time and Date:_____

Name of Exhibit:_____

Type of Animal:_____

Interesting Observations:

_____
_____
_____
_____
_____
_____
_____

# Today I saw a:

29

## Draw its natural habitat:

## Draw its enclosure:

## My Notes:

_____
_____
_____
_____
_____
_____
_____
_____
_____
_____
_____
_____
_____

## Meal at the zoo:

## Meal in the wild:

Name of Zoo:_____

City and State:_____

Time and Date:_____

Name of Exhibit:_____

Type of Animal:_____

Interesting Observations:

_____
_____
_____
_____
_____
_____

Today I saw a:

Draw its natural habitat:

Draw its enclosure:

My Notes:

_____
_____
_____
_____
_____
_____
_____
_____
_____
_____
_____
_____

Meal at the zoo:

Meal in the wild:

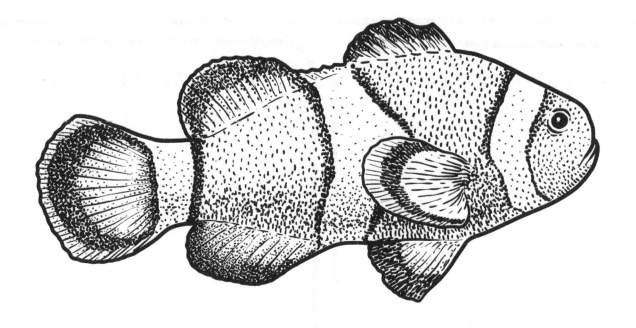

Name of Zoo:_____

City and State:_____

Time and Date:_____

Name of Exhibit:_____

Type of Animal:_____

Interesting Observations:

_____
_____
_____
_____
_____
_____

Today I saw a:

Draw its natural habitat:

Draw its enclosure:

My Notes:

_____
_____
_____
_____
_____
_____
_____
_____
_____
_____
_____
_____
_____

Meal at the zoo:

Meal in the wild:

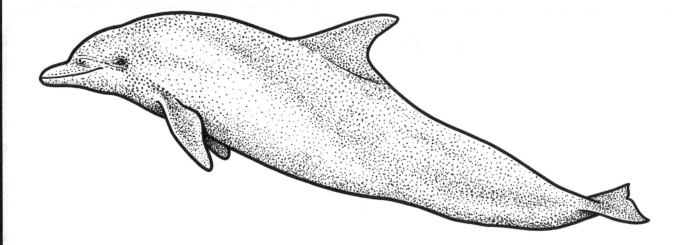

Name of Zoo:_____

City and State:_____

Time and Date:_____

Name of Exhibit:_____

Type of Animal:_____

### Interesting Observations:

_____
_____
_____
_____
_____
_____

Today I saw a:

Draw its natural habitat:

Draw its enclosure:

My Notes:

_____
_____
_____
_____
_____
_____
_____
_____
_____
_____
_____
_____
_____

Meal at the zoo:

Meal in the wild:

Name of Zoo:_____

City and State:_____

Time and Date:_____

Name of Exhibit:_____

Type of Animal:_____

Interesting Observations:

_____
_____
_____
_____
_____
_____

Today I saw a:

Draw its natural habitat:

Draw its enclosure:

My Notes:

_____
_____
_____
_____
_____
_____
_____
_____
_____
_____
_____
_____
_____

Meal at the zoo:

Meal in the wild:

Name of Zoo:_____

City and State:_____

Time and Date:_____

Name of Exhibit:_____

Type of Animal:_____

Interesting Observations:

_____
_____
_____
_____
_____
_____
_____

Today I saw a:

Draw its natural habitat:

Draw its enclosure:

My Notes:

_____
_____
_____
_____
_____
_____
_____
_____
_____
_____
_____
_____

Meal at the zoo:

Meal in the wild:

Name of Zoo:_____

City and State:_____

Time and Date:_____

Name of Exhibit:_____

Type of Animal:_____

Interesting Observations:

_____
_____
_____
_____
_____
_____

# Today I saw a:

## Draw its natural habitat:

## Draw its enclosure:

## My Notes:

_____
_____
_____
_____
_____
_____
_____
_____
_____
_____
_____
_____
_____

## Meal at the zoo:

## Meal in the wild:

Name of Zoo:_____

City and State:_____

Time and Date:_____

Name of Exhibit:_____

Type of Animal:_____

### Interesting Observations:

_____
_____
_____
_____
_____
_____
_____

## Today I saw a:

## Draw its natural habitat:

## Draw its enclosure:

## My Notes:

_____

_____

_____

_____

_____

_____

_____

_____

_____

_____

_____

## Meal at the zoo:

## Meal in the wild:

Name of Zoo:_____

City and State: _____

Time and Date:_____

Name of Exhibit:_____

Type of Animal:_____

Interesting Observations:

_____
_____
_____
_____
_____
_____

Today I saw a:

Draw its natural habitat:

Draw its enclosure:

My Notes:

_____
_____
_____
_____
_____
_____
_____
_____
_____
_____
_____
_____

Meal at the zoo:

Meal in the wild:

Name of Zoo:_____

City and State: _____

Time and Date:_____

Name of Exhibit:_____

Type of Animal:_____

## Interesting Observations:

_____
_____
_____
_____
_____
_____
_____

Today I saw a:

Draw its natural habitat:

Draw its enclosure:

My Notes:

_____
_____
_____
_____
_____
_____
_____
_____
_____
_____
_____
_____
_____

Meal at the zoo:

Meal in the wild:

Name of Zoo:_____

City and State:_____

Time and Date:_____

Name of Exhibit:_____

Type of Animal:_____

Interesting Observations:

_____
_____
_____
_____
_____
_____

Today I saw a:

Draw its natural habitat:

Draw its enclosure:

My Notes:

_____
_____
_____
_____
_____
_____
_____
_____
_____
_____
_____
_____

Meal at the zoo:

Meal in the wild:

Name of Zoo:_____

City and State:_____

Time and Date:_____

Name of Exhibit:_____

Type of Animal:_____

Interesting Observations:

_____
_____
_____
_____
_____
_____

Today I saw a:

Draw its natural habitat:

Draw its enclosure:

My Notes:

_____
_____
_____
_____
_____
_____
_____
_____
_____
_____
_____

Meal at the zoo:

Meal in the wild:

Name of Zoo:_____

City and State:_____

Time and Date:_____

Name of Exhibit:_____

Type of Animal:_____

Interesting Observations:

_____
_____
_____
_____
_____
_____

Today I saw a:

Draw its natural habitat:

Draw its enclosure:

My Notes:

_____
_____
_____
_____
_____
_____
_____
_____
_____
_____
_____
_____
_____

Meal at the zoo:

Meal in the wild:

Name of Zoo:_____

City and State: _____

Time and Date:_____

Name of Exhibit:_____

Type of Animal:_____

Interesting Observations:

_____
_____
_____
_____
_____
_____

## Today I saw a:

## Draw its natural habitat:

## Draw its enclosure:

## My Notes:

_____
_____
_____
_____
_____
_____
_____
_____
_____
_____
_____
_____
_____

## Meal at the zoo:

## Meal in the wild:

Name of Zoo:_____

City and State: _____

Time and Date:_____

Name of Exhibit:_____

Type of Animal:_____

Interesting Observations:

_____
_____
_____
_____
_____
_____

Today I saw a:

57

Draw its natural habitat:

Draw its enclosure:

My Notes:

_____
_____
_____
_____
_____
_____
_____
_____
_____
_____
_____
_____
_____

Meal at the zoo:

Meal in the wild:

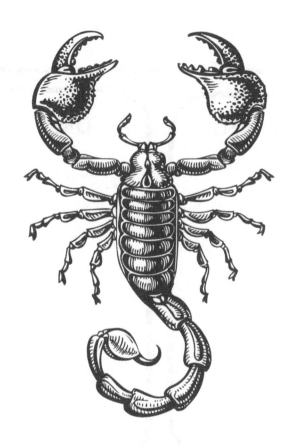

Name of Zoo:_____

City and State:_____

Time and Date:_____

Name of Exhibit:_____

Type of Animal:_____

### Interesting Observations:

_____
_____
_____
_____
_____
_____

Today I saw a:

Draw its natural habitat:

Draw its enclosure:

My Notes:

_____
_____
_____
_____
_____
_____
_____
_____
_____
_____
_____

Meal at the zoo:

Meal in the wild:

Name of Zoo:_____

City and State: _____

Time and Date:_____

Name of Exhibit:_____

Type of Animal:_____

### Interesting Observations:

_____
_____
_____
_____
_____
_____

Today I saw a:

Draw its natural habitat:

Draw its enclosure:

My Notes:

_____
_____
_____
_____
_____
_____
_____
_____
_____
_____
_____
_____

Meal at the zoo:

Meal in the wild:

Name of Zoo:_____

City and State:_____

Time and Date:_____

Name of Exhibit:_____

Type of Animal:_____

Interesting Observations:

_____
_____
_____
_____
_____
_____

# Today I saw a:

## Draw its natural habitat:

## Draw its enclosure:

## My Notes:

_____
_____
_____
_____
_____
_____
_____
_____
_____
_____
_____

## Meal at the zoo:

## Meal in the wild:

Name of Zoo:_____

City and State: _____

Time and Date:_____

Name of Exhibit:_____

Type of Animal:_____

Interesting Observations:

_____
_____
_____
_____
_____
_____
_____

Today I saw a:

Draw its natural habitat:

Draw its enclosure:

My Notes:

_____
_____
_____
_____
_____
_____
_____
_____
_____
_____
_____

Meal at the zoo:

Meal in the wild:

Name of Zoo:_____

City and State:_____

Time and Date:_____

Name of Exhibit:_____

Type of Animal:_____

Interesting Observations:

_____
_____
_____
_____
_____
_____
_____

Today I saw a:

Draw its natural habitat:

Draw its enclosure:

My Notes:

_____

_____

_____

_____

_____

_____

_____

_____

_____

_____

_____

Meal at the zoo:

Meal in the wild:

Name of Zoo:_____

City and State:_____

Time and Date:_____

Name of Exhibit:_____

Type of Animal:_____

### Interesting Observations:

_____
_____
_____
_____
_____
_____
_____

## Today I saw a:

## Draw its natural habitat:

## Draw its enclosure:

## My Notes:

_____
_____
_____
_____
_____
_____
_____
_____
_____
_____
_____
_____

## Meal at the zoo:

## Meal in the wild:

Name of Zoo:_____

City and State:_____

Time and Date:_____

Name of Exhibit:_____

Type of Animal:_____

Interesting Observations:

_____
_____
_____
_____
_____
_____
_____

Today I saw a:

Draw its natural habitat:

Draw its enclosure:

My Notes:

_____
_____
_____
_____
_____
_____
_____
_____
_____
_____
_____

Meal at the zoo:

Meal in the wild:

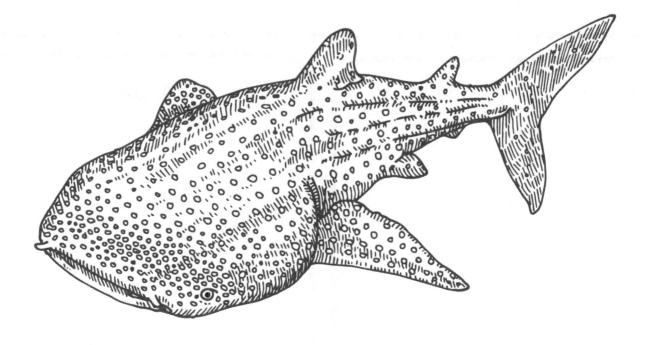

Name of Zoo:_____

City and State:_____

Time and Date:_____

Name of Exhibit:_____

Type of Animal:_____

Interesting Observations:

_____
_____
_____
_____
_____
_____

Today I saw a:

Draw its natural habitat:

Draw its enclosure:

My Notes:

_____
_____
_____
_____
_____
_____
_____
_____
_____
_____
_____
_____

Meal at the zoo:

Meal in the wild:

Name of Zoo:_____

City and State:_____

Time and Date:_____

Name of Exhibit:_____

Type of Animal:_____

Interesting Observations:

_____
_____
_____
_____
_____
_____

Today I saw a:

Draw its natural habitat:

Draw its enclosure:

My Notes:

_____
_____
_____
_____
_____
_____
_____
_____
_____
_____
_____
_____

Meal at the zoo:

Meal in the wild:

Name of Zoo:_____

City and State:_____

Time and Date:_____

Name of Exhibit:_____

Type of Animal:_____

### Interesting Observations:

_____
_____
_____
_____
_____
_____
_____

Today I saw a:

Draw its natural habitat:

Draw its enclosure:

My Notes:

_____
_____
_____
_____
_____
_____
_____
_____
_____
_____
_____

Meal at the zoo:

Meal in the wild:

78

Name of Zoo:_____

City and State:_____

Time and Date:_____

Name of Exhibit:_____

Type of Animal:_____

Interesting Observations:

_____
_____
_____
_____
_____
_____
_____

Today I saw a:

Draw its natural habitat:

Draw its enclosure:

My Notes:

_____
_____
_____
_____
_____
_____
_____
_____
_____
_____
_____
_____

Meal at the zoo:

Meal in the wild:

Name of Zoo:_____

City and State:_____

Time and Date:_____

Name of Exhibit:_____

Type of Animal:_____

Interesting Observations:

_____
_____
_____
_____
_____
_____

Today I saw a:

Draw its natural habitat:

Draw its enclosure:

My Notes:

_____
_____
_____
_____
_____
_____
_____
_____
_____
_____
_____
_____
_____

Meal at the zoo:

Meal in the wild:

Name of Zoo:_____

City and State:_____

Time and Date:_____

Name of Exhibit:_____

Type of Animal:_____

Interesting Observations:

_____
_____
_____
_____
_____
_____
_____

# Today I saw a:

## Draw its natural habitat:

## Draw its enclosure:

## My Notes:

_____
_____
_____
_____
_____
_____
_____
_____
_____
_____
_____

## Meal at the zoo:

## Meal in the wild:

Name of Zoo:_____

City and State:_____

Time and Date:_____

Name of Exhibit:_____

Type of Animal:_____

Interesting Observations:

_____
_____
_____
_____
_____
_____

Today I saw a:

Draw its natural habitat:

Draw its enclosure:

My Notes:

_____
_____
_____
_____
_____
_____
_____
_____
_____
_____
_____
_____

Meal at the zoo:

Meal in the wild:

86

Name of Zoo:_____

City and State:_____

Time and Date:_____

Name of Exhibit:_____

Type of Animal:_____

Interesting Observations:

_____
_____
_____
_____
_____
_____

# Today I saw a:

## Draw its natural habitat:

## Draw its enclosure:

## My Notes:

_____
_____
_____
_____
_____
_____
_____
_____
_____
_____
_____
_____

## Meal at the zoo:

## Meal in the wild:

Name of Zoo:_____

City and State:_____

Time and Date:_____

Name of Exhibit:_____

Type of Animal:_____

Interesting Observations:

_____
_____
_____
_____
_____
_____
_____

Today I saw a:

Draw its natural habitat:

Draw its enclosure:

My Notes:

_____
_____
_____
_____
_____
_____
_____
_____
_____
_____
_____
_____

Meal at the zoo:

Meal in the wild:

Name of Zoo:_____

City and State:_____

Time and Date:_____

Name of Exhibit:_____

Type of Animal:_____

Interesting Observations:

_____
_____
_____
_____
_____
_____

Today I saw a:

Draw its natural habitat:

Draw its enclosure:

My Notes:

_____
_____
_____
_____
_____
_____
_____
_____
_____
_____
_____
_____

Meal at the zoo:

Meal in the wild:

Name of Zoo:_____

City and State:_____

Time and Date:_____

Name of Exhibit:_____

Type of Animal:_____

### Interesting Observations:

_____
_____
_____
_____
_____
_____
_____

## Today I saw a:

## Draw its natural habitat:

## Draw its enclosure:

## My Notes:

_____
_____
_____
_____
_____
_____
_____
_____
_____
_____
_____

## Meal at the zoo:

## Meal in the wild:

Name of Zoo:_____

City and State:_____

Time and Date:_____

Name of Exhibit:_____

Type of Animal:_____

Interesting Observations:

_____
_____
_____
_____
_____
_____
_____

Today I saw a:

Draw its natural habitat:

Draw its enclosure:

My Notes:

_____
_____
_____
_____
_____
_____
_____
_____
_____
_____
_____

Meal at the zoo:

Meal in the wild:

Name of Zoo:_____

City and State:_____

Time and Date:_____

Name of Exhibit:_____

Type of Animal:_____

### Interesting Observations:

_____
_____
_____
_____
_____
_____
_____

# Today I saw a:

## Draw its natural habitat:

## Draw its enclosure:

## My Notes:

_____
_____
_____
_____
_____
_____
_____
_____
_____
_____
_____

## Meal at the zoo:

## Meal in the wild:

Name of Zoo:_____

City and State:_____

Time and Date:_____

Name of Exhibit:_____

Type of Animal:_____

## Interesting Observations:

_____
_____
_____
_____
_____
_____

Today I saw a:

Draw its natural habitat:

Draw its enclosure:

My Notes:

_____
_____
_____
_____
_____
_____
_____
_____
_____
_____
_____

Meal at the zoo:

Meal in the wild:

Name of Zoo:_____

City and State:_____

Time and Date:_____

Name of Exhibit:_____

Type of Animal:_____

Interesting Observations:

_____
_____
_____
_____
_____
_____
_____

## Today I saw a:

## Draw its natural habitat:

## Draw its enclosure:

## My Notes:

_____
_____
_____
_____
_____
_____
_____
_____
_____
_____
_____

## Meal at the zoo:

## Meal in the wild:

Name of Zoo:_____

City and State:_____

Time and Date:_____

Name of Exhibit:_____

Type of Animal:_____

Interesting Observations:

_____
_____
_____
_____
_____
_____

# Today I saw a:

## Draw its natural habitat:

## Draw its enclosure:

## My Notes:

_____
_____
_____
_____
_____
_____
_____
_____
_____
_____
_____
_____

## Meal at the zoo:

## Meal in the wild:

104

Name of Zoo:_____

City and State:_____

Time and Date:_____

Name of Exhibit:_____

Type of Animal:_____

Interesting Observations:

_____
_____
_____
_____
_____
_____
_____

Today I saw a:

Draw its natural habitat:

Draw its enclosure:

My Notes:

_____
_____
_____
_____
_____
_____
_____
_____
_____
_____
_____
_____

Meal at the zoo:

Meal in the wild:

106

Made in United States
Orlando, FL
22 March 2024

45068271R00059